Pomegranate

SAN FRANCISCO

Published by Pomegranate Communications, Inc.
Box 6099, Rohnert Park, CA 94927
800-227-1428; www.pomegranate.com

Pomegranate Europe Ltd.
Fullbridge House, Fullbridge
Maldon, Essex CM9 4LE, England

Claude Monet (1840–1926)
The Artist's Garden in Argenteuil
(A Corner of the Garden with Dahlias), 1873
Oil on canvas, 61 x 82.5 cm
National Gallery of Art, Washington
Gift (Partial and Promised) of Janice H. Levin,
in Honor of the 50th Anniversary of the
National Gallery of Art 1991.27.1

Designed by Barbara Derringer
Printed in China

ISBN 0-7649-1274-7
Catalog No. A987

NAME

ADDRESS

(H)☎ CELL/PGR

(W)☎ FAX

E-MAIL

NAME

ADDRESS

(H)☎ CELL/PGR

(W)☎ FAX

E-MAIL

NAME

ADDRESS

(H)☎ CELL/PGR

(W)☎ FAX

E-MAIL

NAME

ADDRESS

(H)☎ CELL/PGR

(W)☎ FAX

E-MAIL

NAME

ADDRESS

(H)☎ CELL/PGR

(W)☎ FAX

E-MAIL

NAME

ADDRESS

(H)☎ CELL/PGR

(W)☎ FAX

E-MAIL

NAME

ADDRESS

(H)☎ CELL/PGR

(W)☎ FAX

E-MAIL

NAME

ADDRESS

(H)☎ CELL/PGR

(W)☎ FAX

E-MAIL

NAME

ADDRESS

(H)☎ CELL/PGR

(W)☎ FAX

E-MAIL

NAME

ADDRESS

(H)☎ CELL/PGR

(W)☎ FAX

E-MAIL

NAME

ADDRESS

(H)☎ CELL/PGR

(W)☎ FAX

E-MAIL

NAME

ADDRESS

(H)☎ CELL/PGR

(W)☎ FAX

E-MAIL

NAME

ADDRESS

(H)☎ CELL/PGR

(W)☎ FAX

E-MAIL

NAME

ADDRESS

(H)☎ CELL/PGR

(W)☎ FAX

E-MAIL

NAME

ADDRESS

(H)☎ CELL/PGR

(W)☎ FAX

E-MAIL

NAME

ADDRESS

(H)☎ CELL/PGR

(W)☎ FAX

E-MAIL

NAME

ADDRESS

(H)☎ CELL/PGR

(W)☎ FAX

E-MAIL

NAME

ADDRESS

(H)☎ CELL/PGR

(W)☎ FAX

E-MAIL

NAME

ADDRESS

(H)☎ CELL/PGR

(W)☎ FAX

E-MAIL

NAME

ADDRESS

(H)☎ CELL/PGR

(W)☎ FAX

E-MAIL

NAME

ADDRESS

(H)☎ CELL/PGR

(W)☎ FAX

E-MAIL

NAME

ADDRESS

(H)☎ CELL/PGR

(W)☎ FAX

E-MAIL

NAME

ADDRESS

(H)☎ CELL/PGR

(W)☎ FAX

E-MAIL

NAME

ADDRESS

(H)☎ CELL/PGR

(W)☎ FAX

E-MAIL

NAME

ADDRESS

(H)☎ CELL/PGR

(W)☎ FAX

E-MAIL

NAME

ADDRESS

(H)☎ CELL/PGR

(W)☎ FAX

E-MAIL

NAME

ADDRESS

(H)☎ CELL/PGR

(W)☎ FAX

E-MAIL

NAME

ADDRESS

(H)☎ CELL/PGR

(W)☎ FAX

E-MAIL

NAME

ADDRESS

(H) ☎ CELL/PGR

(W) ☎ FAX

E-MAIL

NAME

ADDRESS

(H) ☎ CELL/PGR

(W) ☎ FAX

E-MAIL

NAME

ADDRESS

(H) ☎ CELL/PGR

(W) ☎ FAX

E-MAIL

NAME

ADDRESS

(H) ☎ CELL/PGR

(W) ☎ FAX

E-MAIL

NAME

ADDRESS

(H)☎ CELL/PGR

(W)☎ FAX

E-MAIL

NAME

ADDRESS

(H)☎ CELL/PGR

(W)☎ FAX

E-MAIL

NAME

ADDRESS

(H)☎ CELL/PGR

(W)☎ FAX

E-MAIL

NAME

ADDRESS

(H)☎ CELL/PGR

(W)☎ FAX

E-MAIL

NAME

ADDRESS

(H)☎ CELL/PGR

(W)☎ FAX

E-MAIL

NAME

ADDRESS

(H)☎ CELL/PGR

(W)☎ FAX

E-MAIL

NAME

ADDRESS

(H)☎ CELL/PGR

(W)☎ FAX

E-MAIL

NAME

ADDRESS

(H)☎ CELL/PGR

(W)☎ FAX

E-MAIL

NAME

ADDRESS

(H)☎ CELL/PGR

(W)☎ FAX

E-MAIL

NAME

ADDRESS

(H)☎ CELL/PGR

(W)☎ FAX

E-MAIL

NAME

ADDRESS

(H)☎ CELL/PGR

(W)☎ FAX

E-MAIL

NAME

ADDRESS

(H)☎ CELL/PGR

(W)☎ FAX

E-MAIL

NAME

ADDRESS

(H)☎ CELL/PGR

(W)☎ FAX

E-MAIL

NAME

ADDRESS

(H)☎ CELL/PGR

(W)☎ FAX

E-MAIL

NAME

ADDRESS

(H)☎ CELL/PGR

(W)☎ FAX

E-MAIL

NAME

ADDRESS

(H)☎ CELL/PGR

(W)☎ FAX

E-MAIL

NAME

ADDRESS

(H)☎ CELL/PGR

(W)☎ FAX

E-MAIL

NAME

ADDRESS

(H)☎ CELL/PGR

(W)☎ FAX

E-MAIL

NAME

ADDRESS

(H)☎ CELL/PGR

(W)☎ FAX

E-MAIL

NAME

ADDRESS

(H)☎ CELL/PGR

(W)☎ FAX

E-MAIL

NAME

ADDRESS

(H)☎ CELL/PGR

(W)☎ FAX

E-MAIL

NAME

ADDRESS

(H)☎ CELL/PGR

(W)☎ FAX

E-MAIL

NAME

ADDRESS

(H)☎ CELL/PGR

(W)☎ FAX

E-MAIL

NAME

ADDRESS

(H)☎ CELL/PGR

(W)☎ FAX

E-MAIL

NAME

ADDRESS

(H) ☎ CELL/PGR

(W) ☎ FAX

E-MAIL

NAME

ADDRESS

(H) ☎ CELL/PGR

(W) ☎ FAX

E-MAIL

NAME

ADDRESS

(H) ☎ CELL/PGR

(W) ☎ FAX

E-MAIL

NAME

ADDRESS

(H) ☎ CELL/PGR

(W) ☎ FAX

E-MAIL

NAME

ADDRESS

(H)☎ CELL/PGR

(W)☎ FAX

E-MAIL

NAME

ADDRESS

(H)☎ CELL/PGR

(W)☎ FAX

E-MAIL

NAME

ADDRESS

(H)☎ CELL/PGR

(W)☎ FAX

E-MAIL

NAME

ADDRESS

(H)☎ CELL/PGR

(W)☎ FAX

E-MAIL

NAME

ADDRESS

(H)☎ CELL/PGR

(W)☎ FAX

E-MAIL

NAME

ADDRESS

(H)☎ CELL/PGR

(W)☎ FAX

E-MAIL

NAME

ADDRESS

(H)☎ CELL/PGR

(W)☎ FAX

E-MAIL

NAME

ADDRESS

(H)☎ CELL/PGR

(W)☎ FAX

E-MAIL

NAME

ADDRESS

(H)☎ CELL/PGR

(W)☎ FAX

E-MAIL

NAME

ADDRESS

(H)☎ CELL/PGR

(W)☎ FAX

E-MAIL

NAME

ADDRESS

(H)☎ CELL/PGR

(W)☎ FAX

E-MAIL

NAME

ADDRESS

(H)☎ CELL/PGR

(W)☎ FAX

E-MAIL

NAME

ADDRESS

(H)☎ CELL/PGR

(W)☎ FAX

E-MAIL

NAME

ADDRESS

(H)☎ CELL/PGR

(W)☎ FAX

E-MAIL

NAME

ADDRESS

(H)☎ CELL/PGR

(W)☎ FAX

E-MAIL

NAME

ADDRESS

(H)☎ CELL/PGR

(W)☎ FAX

E-MAIL

NAME

ADDRESS

(H)☎ CELL/PGR

(W)☎ FAX

E-MAIL

NAME

ADDRESS

(H)☎ CELL/PGR

(W)☎ FAX

E-MAIL

NAME

ADDRESS

(H)☎ CELL/PGR

(W)☎ FAX

E-MAIL

NAME

ADDRESS

(H)☎ CELL/PGR

(W)☎ FAX

E-MAIL

NAME Peggy Ferraro

ADDRESS 88 Bassford

LaGrange, IL 60525

(H)☎ 708-354-1494 CELL/PGR 708-790-3129

(W)☎ FAX

E-MAIL

NAME

ADDRESS

(H)☎ CELL/PGR

(W)☎ FAX

E-MAIL

NAME

ADDRESS

(H)☎ CELL/PGR

(W)☎ FAX

E-MAIL

NAME

ADDRESS

(H)☎ CELL/PGR

(W)☎ FAX

E-MAIL

F

NAME

ADDRESS

(H)☎ CELL/PGR

(W)☎ FAX

E-MAIL

NAME

ADDRESS

(H)☎ CELL/PGR

(W)☎ FAX

E-MAIL

NAME

ADDRESS

(H)☎ CELL/PGR

(W)☎ FAX

E-MAIL

NAME

ADDRESS

(H)☎ CELL/PGR

(W)☎ FAX

E-MAIL

NAME

ADDRESS

(H)☎ CELL/PGR

(W)☎ FAX

E-MAIL

NAME

ADDRESS

(H)☎ CELL/PGR

(W)☎ FAX

E-MAIL

NAME

ADDRESS

(H)☎ CELL/PGR

(W)☎ FAX

E-MAIL

NAME

ADDRESS

(H)☎ CELL/PGR

(W)☎ FAX

E-MAIL

NAME

ADDRESS

(H)☎ CELL/PGR

(W)☎ FAX

E-MAIL

NAME

ADDRESS

(H)☎ CELL/PGR

(W)☎ FAX

E-MAIL

NAME

ADDRESS

(H)☎ CELL/PGR

(W)☎ FAX

E-MAIL

NAME

ADDRESS

(H)☎ CELL/PGR

(W)☎ FAX

E-MAIL

NAME Bill & Jann Gullick
ADDRESS 1094 Hammond Dr
Seminole, FL 33774
(H)☎ CELL/PGR 727-776-8528
(W)☎ FAX
E-MAIL

NAME Wally + Sue Gullick
ADDRESS 1769 Oak Forest Dr
New Braunfel, TX 78132
(H)☎ CELL/PGR 830-624-4007
(W)☎ FAX
E-MAIL

NAME
ADDRESS

(H)☎ CELL/PGR
(W)☎ FAX
E-MAIL

NAME
ADDRESS

(H)☎ CELL/PGR
(W)☎ FAX
E-MAIL

G

NAME

ADDRESS

(H)☎ CELL/PGR

(W)☎ FAX

E-MAIL

NAME

ADDRESS

(H)☎ CELL/PGR

(W)☎ FAX

E-MAIL

NAME

ADDRESS

(H)☎ CELL/PGR

(W)☎ FAX

E-MAIL

NAME

ADDRESS

(H)☎ CELL/PGR

(W)☎ FAX

E-MAIL

NAME

ADDRESS

(H)☎ CELL/PGR

(W)☎ FAX

E-MAIL

NAME

ADDRESS

(H)☎ CELL/PGR

(W)☎ FAX

E-MAIL

NAME

ADDRESS

(H)☎ CELL/PGR

(W)☎ FAX

E-MAIL

NAME

ADDRESS

(H)☎ CELL/PGR

(W)☎ FAX

E-MAIL

NAME

ADDRESS

(H) ☎ CELL/PGR

(W) ☎ FAX

E-MAIL

NAME

ADDRESS

(H) ☎ CELL/PGR

(W) ☎ FAX

E-MAIL

NAME

ADDRESS

(H) ☎ CELL/PGR

(W) ☎ FAX

E-MAIL

NAME

ADDRESS

(H) ☎ CELL/PGR

(W) ☎ FAX

E-MAIL

NAME Kevin & Gayle Healy
ADDRESS 6409 So Narragansett
Chicago, IL 60638
(H) 773-229-1322 CELL/PGR
(W) FAX
E-MAIL

NAME Dennis & Rita Healy
ADDRESS 1918 Arthur Ave
Berkley, IL 60163
(H) 630-449-1426 CELL/PGR
(W) FAX
E-MAIL

NAME Bob Colleen Healy
ADDRESS 4140 W 100th Street
Oak Lawn, IL
(H) 630-878-3285 B CELL/PGR 708-372-2592 C
(W) FAX
E-MAIL

NAME Jan & Bob Hillerud
ADDRESS 102 Christine Street
Oswego, IL 60543
(H) CELL/PGR
(W) FAX
E-MAIL

H

NAME

ADDRESS

(H)☎ CELL/PGR

(W)☎ FAX

E-MAIL

NAME

ADDRESS

(H)☎ CELL/PGR

(W)☎ FAX

E-MAIL

NAME

ADDRESS

(H)☎ CELL/PGR

(W)☎ FAX

E-MAIL

NAME

ADDRESS

(H)☎ CELL/PGR

(W)☎ FAX

E-MAIL

NAME

ADDRESS

(H) ☎ CELL/PGR

(W) ☎ FAX

E-MAIL

NAME

ADDRESS

(H) ☎ CELL/PGR

(W) ☎ FAX

E-MAIL

NAME

ADDRESS

(H) ☎ CELL/PGR

(W) ☎ FAX

E-MAIL

NAME

ADDRESS

(H) ☎ CELL/PGR

(W) ☎ FAX

E-MAIL

NAME

ADDRESS

(H) ☎ CELL/PGR

(W) ☎ FAX

E-MAIL

NAME

ADDRESS

(H) ☎ CELL/PGR

(W) ☎ FAX

E-MAIL

NAME

ADDRESS

(H) ☎ CELL/PGR

(W) ☎ FAX

E-MAIL

NAME

ADDRESS

(H) ☎ CELL/PGR

(W) ☎ FAX

E-MAIL

NAME

ADDRESS

(H)☎ CELL/PGR

(W)☎ FAX

E-MAIL

NAME

ADDRESS

(H)☎ CELL/PGR

(W)☎ FAX

E-MAIL

NAME

ADDRESS

(H)☎ CELL/PGR

(W)☎ FAX

E-MAIL

NAME

ADDRESS

(H)☎ CELL/PGR

(W)☎ FAX

E-MAIL

NAME

ADDRESS

(H) ☎ CELL/PGR

(W) ☎ FAX

E-MAIL

NAME

ADDRESS

(H) ☎ CELL/PGR

(W) ☎ FAX

E-MAIL

NAME

ADDRESS

(H) ☎ CELL/PGR

(W) ☎ FAX

E-MAIL

NAME

ADDRESS

(H) ☎ CELL/PGR

(W) ☎ FAX

E-MAIL

NAME

ADDRESS

(H)☎ CELL/PGR

(W)☎ FAX

E-MAIL

NAME

ADDRESS

(H)☎ CELL/PGR

(W)☎ FAX

E-MAIL

NAME

ADDRESS

(H)☎ CELL/PGR

(W)☎ FAX

E-MAIL

NAME

ADDRESS

(H)☎ CELL/PGR

(W)☎ FAX

E-MAIL

NAME

ADDRESS

(H) ☎ CELL/PGR

(W) ☎ FAX

E-MAIL

NAME

ADDRESS

(H) ☎ CELL/PGR

(W) ☎ FAX

E-MAIL

NAME

ADDRESS

(H) ☎ CELL/PGR

(W) ☎ FAX

E-MAIL

NAME

ADDRESS

(H) ☎ CELL/PGR

(W) ☎ FAX

E-MAIL

NAME

ADDRESS

(H)☎ CELL/PGR

(W)☎ FAX

E-MAIL

NAME

ADDRESS

(H)☎ CELL/PGR

(W)☎ FAX

E-MAIL

NAME

ADDRESS

(H)☎ CELL/PGR

(W)☎ FAX

E-MAIL

NAME

ADDRESS

(H)☎ CELL/PGR

(W)☎ FAX

E-MAIL

NAME

ADDRESS

(H)☎ CELL/PGR

(W)☎ FAX

E-MAIL

NAME

ADDRESS

(H)☎ CELL/PGR

(W)☎ FAX

E-MAIL

NAME

ADDRESS

(H)☎ CELL/PGR

(W)☎ FAX

E-MAIL

NAME

ADDRESS

(H)☎ CELL/PGR

(W)☎ FAX

E-MAIL

NAME

ADDRESS

(H) ☎ CELL/PGR

(W) ☎ FAX

E-MAIL

NAME

ADDRESS

(H) ☎ CELL/PGR

(W) ☎ FAX

E-MAIL

NAME

ADDRESS

(H) ☎ CELL/PGR

(W) ☎ FAX

E-MAIL

NAME

ADDRESS

(H) ☎ CELL/PGR

(W) ☎ FAX

E-MAIL

NAME

ADDRESS

(H)☎ CELL/PGR

(W)☎ FAX

E-MAIL

NAME

ADDRESS

(H)☎ CELL/PGR

(W)☎ FAX

E-MAIL

NAME

ADDRESS

(H)☎ CELL/PGR

(W)☎ FAX

E-MAIL

NAME

ADDRESS

(H)☎ CELL/PGR

(W)☎ FAX

E-MAIL

NAME June Kaduk
ADDRESS 6138 WillowHill Rd #B
Willowbrook, IL 60527
(H) 630-908-7122 CELL/PGR
(W) FAX
E-MAIL

NAME Jack & Bunny Kaduk
ADDRESS 6N387 W/Ridgewood
St. Charles, IL 60175
(H) CELL/PGR
(W) FAX
E-MAIL

NAME
ADDRESS

(H) CELL/PGR
(W) FAX
E-MAIL

NAME
ADDRESS

(H) CELL/PGR
(W) FAX
E-MAIL

K

NAME

ADDRESS

(H) ☎ CELL/PGR

(W) ☎ FAX

E-MAIL

NAME

ADDRESS

(H) ☎ CELL/PGR

(W) ☎ FAX

E-MAIL

NAME

ADDRESS

(H) ☎ CELL/PGR

(W) ☎ FAX

E-MAIL

NAME

ADDRESS

(H) ☎ CELL/PGR

(W) ☎ FAX

E-MAIL

NAME

ADDRESS

(H)☎ CELL/PGR

(W)☎ FAX

E-MAIL

NAME

ADDRESS

(H)☎ CELL/PGR

(W)☎ FAX

E-MAIL

NAME

ADDRESS

(H)☎ CELL/PGR

(W)☎ FAX

E-MAIL

NAME

ADDRESS

(H)☎ CELL/PGR

(W)☎ FAX

E-MAIL

NAME

ADDRESS

(H)☎ CELL/PGR

(W)☎ FAX

E-MAIL

NAME

ADDRESS

(H)☎ CELL/PGR

(W)☎ FAX

E-MAIL

NAME

ADDRESS

(H)☎ CELL/PGR

(W)☎ FAX

E-MAIL

NAME

ADDRESS

(H)☎ CELL/PGR

(W)☎ FAX

E-MAIL

NAME

ADDRESS

(H)☎ CELL/PGR

(W)☎ FAX

E-MAIL

NAME

ADDRESS

(H)☎ CELL/PGR

(W)☎ FAX

E-MAIL

NAME

ADDRESS

(H)☎ CELL/PGR

(W)☎ FAX

E-MAIL

NAME

ADDRESS

(H)☎ CELL/PGR

(W)☎ FAX

E-MAIL

NAME

ADDRESS

(H) ☎ CELL/PGR

(W) ☎ FAX

E-MAIL

NAME

ADDRESS

(H) ☎ CELL/PGR

(W) ☎ FAX

E-MAIL

NAME

ADDRESS

(H) ☎ CELL/PGR

(W) ☎ FAX

E-MAIL

NAME

ADDRESS

(H) ☎ CELL/PGR

(W) ☎ FAX

E-MAIL

NAME

ADDRESS

(H)☎ CELL/PGR

(W)☎ FAX

E-MAIL

NAME

ADDRESS

(H)☎ CELL/PGR

(W)☎ FAX

E-MAIL

NAME

ADDRESS

(H)☎ CELL/PGR

(W)☎ FAX

E-MAIL

NAME

ADDRESS

(H)☎ CELL/PGR

(W)☎ FAX

E-MAIL

NAME

ADDRESS

(H) ☎ CELL/PGR

(W) ☎ FAX

E-MAIL

NAME

ADDRESS

(H) ☎ CELL/PGR

(W) ☎ FAX

E-MAIL

NAME

ADDRESS

(H) ☎ CELL/PGR

(W) ☎ FAX

E-MAIL

NAME

ADDRESS

(H) ☎ CELL/PGR

(W) ☎ FAX

E-MAIL

NAME

ADDRESS

(H)☎ CELL/PGR

(W.)☎ FAX

E-MAIL

NAME

ADDRESS

(H)☎ CELL/PGR

(W)☎ FAX

E-MAIL

NAME

ADDRESS

(H)☎ CELL/PGR

(W)☎ FAX

E-MAIL

NAME

ADDRESS

(H)☎ CELL/PGR

(W)☎ FAX

E-MAIL

NAME

ADDRESS

(H)☎ CELL/PGR

(W)☎ FAX

E-MAIL

NAME

ADDRESS

(H)☎ CELL/PGR

(W)☎ FAX

E-MAIL

NAME

ADDRESS

(H)☎ CELL/PGR

(W)☎ FAX

E-MAIL

NAME

ADDRESS

(H)☎ CELL/PGR

(W)☎ FAX

E-MAIL

NAME

ADDRESS

(H)☎ CELL/PGR

(W)☎ FAX

E-MAIL

NAME

ADDRESS

(H)☎ CELL/PGR

(W)☎ FAX

E-MAIL

NAME

ADDRESS

(H)☎ CELL/PGR

(W)☎ FAX

E-MAIL

NAME

ADDRESS

(H)☎ CELL/PGR

(W)☎ FAX

E-MAIL

NAME

ADDRESS

(H)☎ CELL/PGR

(W)☎ FAX

E-MAIL

NAME

ADDRESS

(H)☎ CELL/PGR

(W)☎ FAX

E-MAIL

NAME

ADDRESS

(H)☎ CELL/PGR

(W)☎ FAX

E-MAIL

NAME

ADDRESS

(H)☎ CELL/PGR

(W)☎ FAX

E-MAIL

NAME

ADDRESS

(H) ☎ CELL/PGR

(W) ☎ FAX

E-MAIL

NAME

ADDRESS

(H) ☎ CELL/PGR

(W) ☎ FAX

E-MAIL

NAME

ADDRESS

(H) ☎ CELL/PGR

(W) ☎ FAX

E-MAIL

NAME

ADDRESS

(H) ☎ CELL/PGR

(W) ☎ FAX

E-MAIL

NAME

ADDRESS

(H)☎ CELL/PGR

(W)☎ FAX

E-MAIL

NAME

ADDRESS

(H)☎ CELL/PGR

(W)☎ FAX

E-MAIL

NAME

ADDRESS

(H)☎ CELL/PGR

(W)☎ FAX

E-MAIL

NAME

ADDRESS

(H)☎ CELL/PGR

(W)☎ FAX

E-MAIL

NAME

ADDRESS

(H)☎ CELL/PGR

(W)☎ FAX

E-MAIL

NAME

ADDRESS

(H)☎ CELL/PGR

(W)☎ FAX

E-MAIL

NAME

ADDRESS

(H)☎ CELL/PGR

(W)☎ FAX

E-MAIL

NAME

ADDRESS

(H)☎ CELL/PGR

(W)☎ FAX

E-MAIL

NAME

ADDRESS

(H)☎ CELL/PGR

(W)☎ FAX

E-MAIL

NAME

ADDRESS

(H)☎ CELL/PGR

(W)☎ FAX

E-MAIL

NAME

ADDRESS

(H)☎ CELL/PGR

(W)☎ FAX

E-MAIL

NAME

ADDRESS

(H)☎ CELL/PGR

(W)☎ FAX

E-MAIL

NAME

ADDRESS

(H)☎ CELL/PGR

(W)☎ FAX

E-MAIL

NAME

ADDRESS

(H)☎ CELL/PGR

(W)☎ FAX

E-MAIL

NAME

ADDRESS

(H)☎ CELL/PGR

(W)☎ FAX

E-MAIL

NAME

ADDRESS

(H)☎ CELL/PGR

(W)☎ FAX

E-MAIL

NAME

ADDRESS

(H)☎ CELL/PGR

(W)☎ FAX

E-MAIL

NAME

ADDRESS

(H)☎ CELL/PGR

(W)☎ FAX

E-MAIL

NAME

ADDRESS

(H)☎ CELL/PGR

(W)☎ FAX

E-MAIL

NAME

ADDRESS

(H)☎ CELL/PGR

(W)☎ FAX

E-MAIL

NAME

ADDRESS

(H)☎ CELL/PGR

(W)☎ FAX

E-MAIL

NAME

ADDRESS

(H)☎ CELL/PGR

(W)☎ FAX

E-MAIL

NAME

ADDRESS

(H)☎ CELL/PGR

(W)☎ FAX

E-MAIL

NAME

ADDRESS

(H)☎ CELL/PGR

(W)☎ FAX

E-MAIL

NAME

ADDRESS

(H)☎ CELL/PGR

(W)☎ FAX

E-MAIL

NAME

ADDRESS

(H)☎ CELL/PGR

(W)☎ FAX

E-MAIL

NAME

ADDRESS

(H)☎ CELL/PGR

(W)☎ FAX

E-MAIL

NAME

ADDRESS

(H)☎ CELL/PGR

(W)☎ FAX

E-MAIL

NAME Diane & Mark Pasquinelli
ADDRESS 8900 Vail
Woodridge, IL 60517
(H)☎ CELL/PGR
(W)☎ FAX
E-MAIL

NAME
ADDRESS

(H)☎ CELL/PGR
(W)☎ FAX
E-MAIL

NAME
ADDRESS

(H)☎ CELL/PGR
(W)☎ FAX
E-MAIL

NAME
ADDRESS

(H)☎ CELL/PGR
(W)☎ FAX
E-MAIL

NAME

ADDRESS

(H)☎ CELL/PGR

(W)☎ FAX

E-MAIL

NAME

ADDRESS

(H)☎ CELL/PGR

(W)☎ FAX

E-MAIL

NAME

ADDRESS

(H)☎ CELL/PGR

(W)☎ FAX

E-MAIL

NAME

ADDRESS

(H)☎ CELL/PGR

(W)☎ FAX

E-MAIL

NAME

ADDRESS

(H)☎ CELL/PGR

(W)☎ FAX

E-MAIL

NAME

ADDRESS

(H)☎ CELL/PGR

(W)☎ FAX

E-MAIL

NAME

ADDRESS

(H)☎ CELL/PGR

(W)☎ FAX

E-MAIL

NAME

ADDRESS

(H)☎ CELL/PGR

(W)☎ FAX

E-MAIL

NAME

ADDRESS

(H)☎ CELL/PGR

(W)☎ FAX

E-MAIL

NAME

ADDRESS

(H)☎ CELL/PGR

(W)☎ FAX

E-MAIL

NAME

ADDRESS

(H)☎ CELL/PGR

(W)☎ FAX

E-MAIL

NAME

ADDRESS

(H)☎ CELL/PGR

(W)☎ FAX

E-MAIL

NAME

ADDRESS

(H)☎ CELL/PGR

(W)☎ FAX

E-MAIL

NAME

ADDRESS

(H)☎ CELL/PGR

(W)☎ FAX

E-MAIL

NAME

ADDRESS

(H)☎ CELL/PGR

(W)☎ FAX

E-MAIL

NAME

ADDRESS

(H)☎ CELL/PGR

(W)☎ FAX

E-MAIL

NAME

ADDRESS

(H) ☎ CELL/PGR

(W) ☎ FAX

E-MAIL

NAME

ADDRESS

(H) ☎ CELL/PGR

(W) ☎ FAX

E-MAIL

NAME

ADDRESS

(H) ☎ CELL/PGR

(W) ☎ FAX

E-MAIL

NAME

ADDRESS

(H) ☎ CELL/PGR

(W) ☎ FAX

E-MAIL

NAME

ADDRESS

(H)☎ CELL/PGR

(W)☎ FAX

E-MAIL

NAME

ADDRESS

(H)☎ CELL/PGR

(W)☎ FAX

E-MAIL

NAME

ADDRESS

(H)☎ CELL/PGR

(W)☎ FAX

E-MAIL

NAME

ADDRESS

(H)☎ CELL/PGR

(W)☎ FAX

E-MAIL

NAME

ADDRESS

(H)☎ CELL/PGR

(W)☎ FAX

E-MAIL

NAME

ADDRESS

(H)☎ CELL/PGR

(W)☎ FAX

E-MAIL

NAME

ADDRESS

(H)☎ CELL/PGR

(W)☎ FAX

E-MAIL

NAME

ADDRESS

(H)☎ CELL/PGR

(W)☎ FAX

E-MAIL

NAME Carol Rembles

ADDRESS 10106 So Park Ave

Oaklawn, IL 60453

(H)☎ CELL/PGR

(W)☎ FAX

E-MAIL

NAME

ADDRESS

(H)☎ CELL/PGR

(W)☎ FAX

E-MAIL

NAME

ADDRESS

(H)☎ CELL/PGR

(W)☎ FAX

E-MAIL

NAME

ADDRESS

(H)☎ CELL/PGR

(W)☎ FAX

E-MAIL

R

NAME

ADDRESS

(H)☎ CELL/PGR

(W)☎ FAX

E-MAIL

NAME

ADDRESS

(H)☎ CELL/PGR

(W)☎ FAX

E-MAIL

NAME

ADDRESS

(H)☎ CELL/PGR

(W)☎ FAX

E-MAIL

NAME

ADDRESS

(H)☎ CELL/PGR

(W)☎ FAX

E-MAIL

NAME

ADDRESS

(H)☎ CELL/PGR

(W)☎ FAX

E-MAIL

NAME

ADDRESS

(H)☎ CELL/PGR

(W)☎ FAX

E-MAIL

NAME

ADDRESS

(H)☎ CELL/PGR

(W)☎ FAX

E-MAIL

NAME

ADDRESS

(H)☎ CELL/PGR

(W)☎ FAX

E-MAIL

NAME

ADDRESS

(H)☎ CELL/PGR

(W)☎ FAX

E-MAIL

NAME

ADDRESS

(H)☎ CELL/PGR

(W)☎ FAX

E-MAIL

NAME

ADDRESS

(H)☎ CELL/PGR

(W)☎ FAX

E-MAIL

NAME

ADDRESS

(H)☎ CELL/PGR

(W)☎ FAX

E-MAIL

NAME

ADDRESS

(H)☎ CELL/PGR

(W)☎ FAX

E-MAIL

NAME

ADDRESS

(H)☎ CELL/PGR

(W)☎ FAX

E-MAIL

NAME

ADDRESS

(H)☎ CELL/PGR

(W)☎ FAX

E-MAIL

NAME

ADDRESS

(H)☎ CELL/PGR

(W)☎ FAX

E-MAIL

NAME

ADDRESS

(H)☎ CELL/PGR

(W)☎ FAX

E-MAIL

NAME

ADDRESS

(H)☎ CELL/PGR

(W)☎ FAX

E-MAIL

NAME

ADDRESS

(H)☎ CELL/PGR

(W)☎ FAX

E-MAIL

NAME

ADDRESS

(H)☎ CELL/PGR

(W)☎ FAX

E-MAIL

NAME

ADDRESS

(H)☎ CELL/PGR

(W)☎ FAX

E-MAIL

NAME

ADDRESS

(H)☎ CELL/PGR

(W)☎ FAX

E-MAIL

NAME

ADDRESS

(H)☎ CELL/PGR

(W)☎ FAX

E-MAIL

NAME

ADDRESS

(H)☎ CELL/PGR

(W)☎ FAX

E-MAIL

NAME

ADDRESS

(H)☎ CELL/PGR

(W)☎ FAX

E-MAIL

NAME

ADDRESS

(H)☎ CELL/PGR

(W)☎ FAX

E-MAIL

NAME

ADDRESS

(H)☎ CELL/PGR

(W)☎ FAX

E-MAIL

NAME

ADDRESS

(H)☎ CELL/PGR

(W)☎ FAX

E-MAIL

NAME

ADDRESS

(H)☎ CELL/PGR

(W)☎ FAX

E-MAIL

NAME

ADDRESS

(H)☎ CELL/PGR

(W)☎ FAX

E-MAIL

NAME

ADDRESS

(H)☎ CELL/PGR

(W)☎ FAX

E-MAIL

NAME

ADDRESS

(H)☎ CELL/PGR

(W)☎ FAX

E-MAIL

NAME

ADDRESS

(H)☎ CELL/PGR

(W)☎ FAX

E-MAIL

NAME

ADDRESS

(H)☎ CELL/PGR

(W)☎ FAX

E-MAIL

NAME

ADDRESS

(H)☎ CELL/PGR

(W)☎ FAX

E-MAIL

NAME

ADDRESS

(H)☎ CELL/PGR

(W)☎ FAX

E-MAIL

NAME

ADDRESS

(H) ☎ CELL/PGR

(W) ☎ FAX

E-MAIL

NAME

ADDRESS

(H) ☎ CELL/PGR

(W) ☎ FAX

E-MAIL

NAME

ADDRESS

(H) ☎ CELL/PGR

(W) ☎ FAX

E-MAIL

NAME

ADDRESS

(H) ☎ CELL/PGR

(W) ☎ FAX

E-MAIL

NAME

ADDRESS

(H)☎ CELL/PGR

(W)☎ FAX

E-MAIL

NAME

ADDRESS

(H)☎ CELL/PGR

(W)☎ FAX

E-MAIL

NAME

ADDRESS

(H)☎ CELL/PGR

(W)☎ FAX

E-MAIL

NAME

ADDRESS

(H)☎ CELL/PGR

(W)☎ FAX

E-MAIL

NAME

ADDRESS

(H)☎ CELL/PGR

(W)☎ FAX

E-MAIL

NAME

ADDRESS

(H)☎ CELL/PGR

(W)☎ FAX

E-MAIL

NAME

ADDRESS

(H)☎ CELL/PGR

(W)☎ FAX

E-MAIL

NAME

ADDRESS

(H)☎ CELL/PGR

(W)☎ FAX

E-MAIL

NAME

ADDRESS

(H)☎ CELL/PGR

(W)☎ FAX

E-MAIL

NAME

ADDRESS

(H)☎ CELL/PGR

(W)☎ FAX

E-MAIL

NAME

ADDRESS

(H)☎ CELL/PGR

(W)☎ FAX

E-MAIL

NAME

ADDRESS

(H)☎ CELL/PGR

(W)☎ FAX

E-MAIL

NAME

ADDRESS

(H)☎ CELL/PGR

(W)☎ FAX

E-MAIL

NAME

ADDRESS

(H)☎ CELL/PGR

(W)☎ FAX

E-MAIL

NAME

ADDRESS

(H)☎ CELL/PGR

(W)☎ FAX

E-MAIL

NAME

ADDRESS

(H)☎ CELL/PGR

(W)☎ FAX

E-MAIL

NAME

ADDRESS

(H)☎ CELL/PGR

(W)☎ FAX

E-MAIL

NAME

ADDRESS

(H)☎ CELL/PGR

(W)☎ FAX

E-MAIL

NAME

ADDRESS

(H)☎ CELL/PGR

(W)☎ FAX

E-MAIL

NAME

ADDRESS

(H)☎ CELL/PGR

(W)☎ FAX

E-MAIL

NAME

ADDRESS

(H)☎ CELL/PGR

(W)☎ FAX

E-MAIL

NAME

ADDRESS

(H)☎ CELL/PGR

(W)☎ FAX

E-MAIL

NAME

ADDRESS

(H)☎ CELL/PGR

(W)☎ FAX

E-MAIL

NAME

ADDRESS

(H)☎ CELL/PGR

(W)☎ FAX

E-MAIL

NAME

ADDRESS

(H)☎ CELL/PGR

(W)☎ FAX

E-MAIL

NAME

ADDRESS

(H)☎ CELL/PGR

(W)☎ FAX

E-MAIL

NAME

ADDRESS

(H)☎ CELL/PGR

(W)☎ FAX

E-MAIL

NAME

ADDRESS

(H)☎ CELL/PGR

(W)☎ FAX

E-MAIL

NAME

ADDRESS

(H)☎ CELL/PGR

(W)☎ FAX

E-MAIL

NAME

ADDRESS

(H)☎ CELL/PGR

(W)☎ FAX

E-MAIL

NAME

ADDRESS

(H)☎ CELL/PGR

(W)☎ FAX

E-MAIL

NAME

ADDRESS

(H)☎ CELL/PGR

(W)☎ FAX

E-MAIL

NAME

ADDRESS

(H) ☎ CELL/PGR

(W) ☎ FAX

E-MAIL

NAME

ADDRESS

(H) ☎ CELL/PGR

(W) ☎ FAX

E-MAIL

NAME

ADDRESS

(H) ☎ CELL/PGR

(W) ☎ FAX

E-MAIL

NAME

ADDRESS

(H) ☎ CELL/PGR

(W) ☎ FAX

E-MAIL

NAME

ADDRESS

(H)☎ CELL/PGR

(W)☎ FAX

E-MAIL

NAME

ADDRESS

(H)☎ CELL/PGR

(W)☎ FAX

E-MAIL

NAME

ADDRESS

(H)☎ CELL/PGR

(W)☎ FAX

E-MAIL

NAME

ADDRESS

(H)☎ CELL/PGR

(W)☎ FAX

E-MAIL

NAME

ADDRESS

(H) ☎ CELL/PGR

(W) ☎ FAX

E-MAIL

NAME

ADDRESS

(H) ☎ CELL/PGR

(W) ☎ FAX

E-MAIL

NAME

ADDRESS

(H) ☎ CELL/PGR

(W) ☎ FAX

E-MAIL

NAME

ADDRESS

(H) ☎ CELL/PGR

(W) ☎ FAX

E-MAIL

NAME

ADDRESS

(H)☎ CELL/PGR

(W)☎ FAX

E-MAIL

NAME

ADDRESS

(H)☎ CELL/PGR

(W)☎ FAX

E-MAIL

NAME

ADDRESS

(H)☎ CELL/PGR

(W)☎ FAX

E-MAIL

NAME

ADDRESS

(H)☎ CELL/PGR

(W)☎ FAX

E-MAIL

NAME

ADDRESS

(H) ☎ CELL/PGR

(W) ☎ FAX

E-MAIL

NAME

ADDRESS

(H) ☎ CELL/PGR

(W) ☎ FAX

E-MAIL

NAME

ADDRESS

(H) ☎ CELL/PGR

(W) ☎ FAX

E-MAIL

NAME

ADDRESS

(H) ☎ CELL/PGR

(W) ☎ FAX

E-MAIL

NAME

ADDRESS

(H)☎ CELL/PGR

(W)☎ FAX

E-MAIL

NAME

ADDRESS

(H)☎ CELL/PGR

(W)☎ FAX

E-MAIL

NAME

ADDRESS

(H)☎ CELL/PGR

(W)☎ FAX

E-MAIL

NAME

ADDRESS

(H)☎ CELL/PGR

(W)☎ FAX

E-MAIL

NAME

ADDRESS

(H)☎ CELL/PGR

(W)☎ FAX

E-MAIL

NAME

ADDRESS

(H)☎ CELL/PGR

(W)☎ FAX

E-MAIL

NAME

ADDRESS

(H)☎ CELL/PGR

(W)☎ FAX

E-MAIL

NAME

ADDRESS

(H)☎ CELL/PGR

(W)☎ FAX

E-MAIL

NAME

ADDRESS

(H)☎ CELL/PGR

(W)☎ FAX

E-MAIL

NAME

ADDRESS

(H)☎ CELL/PGR

(W)☎ FAX

E-MAIL

NAME

ADDRESS

(H)☎ CELL/PGR

(W)☎ FAX

E-MAIL

NAME

ADDRESS

(H)☎ CELL/PGR

(W)☎ FAX

E-MAIL

NAME

ADDRESS

(H)☎ CELL/PGR

(W)☎ FAX

E-MAIL

NAME

ADDRESS

(H)☎ CELL/PGR

(W)☎ FAX

E-MAIL

NAME

ADDRESS

(H)☎ CELL/PGR

(W)☎ FAX

E-MAIL

NAME

ADDRESS

(H)☎ CELL/PGR

(W)☎ FAX

E-MAIL

ADDITIONAL ADDRESSES

NAME

ADDRESS

(H)☎ CELL/PGR

(W)☎ FAX

E-MAIL

NAME

ADDRESS

(H)☎ CELL/PGR

(W)☎ FAX

E-MAIL

NAME

ADDRESS

(H)☎ CELL/PGR

(W)☎ FAX

E-MAIL

NAME

ADDRESS

(H) ☎ CELL/PGR

(W) ☎ FAX

E-MAIL

NAME

ADDRESS

(H) ☎ CELL/PGR

(W) ☎ FAX

E-MAIL

NAME

ADDRESS

(H) ☎ CELL/PGR

(W) ☎ FAX

E-MAIL

NAME

ADDRESS

(H) ☎ CELL/PGR

(W) ☎ FAX

E-MAIL

NAME

ADDRESS

(H)☎ CELL/PGR

(W)☎ FAX

E-MAIL

NAME

ADDRESS

(H)☎ CELL/PGR

(W)☎ FAX

E-MAIL

NAME

ADDRESS

(H)☎ CELL/PGR

(W)☎ FAX

E-MAIL

NAME

ADDRESS

(H)☎ CELL/PGR

(W)☎ FAX

E-MAIL

NAME

ADDRESS

(H)☎ CELL/PGR

(W)☎ FAX

E-MAIL

NAME

ADDRESS

(H)☎ CELL/PGR

(W)☎ FAX

E-MAIL

NAME

ADDRESS

(H)☎ CELL/PGR

(W)☎ FAX

E-MAIL

NAME

ADDRESS

(H)☎ CELL/PGR

(W)☎ FAX

E-MAIL

NAME

ADDRESS

(H)☎ CELL/PGR

(W)☎ FAX

E-MAIL

NAME

ADDRESS

(H)☎ CELL/PGR

(W)☎ FAX

E-MAIL

NAME

ADDRESS

(H)☎ CELL/PGR

(W)☎ FAX

E-MAIL

NAME

ADDRESS

(H)☎ CELL/PGR

(W)☎ FAX

E-MAIL

NAME

ADDRESS

(H)☎ CELL/PGR

(W)☎ FAX

E-MAIL

NAME

ADDRESS

(H)☎ CELL/PGR

(W)☎ FAX

E-MAIL

NAME

ADDRESS

(H)☎ CELL/PGR

(W)☎ FAX

E-MAIL

NAME

ADDRESS

(H)☎ CELL/PGR

(W)☎ FAX

E-MAIL

NAME

ADDRESS

(H)☎ CELL/PGR

(W)☎ FAX

E-MAIL

NAME

ADDRESS

(H)☎ CELL/PGR

(W)☎ FAX

E-MAIL

NAME

ADDRESS

(H)☎ CELL/PGR

(W)☎ FAX

E-MAIL

NAME

ADDRESS

(H)☎ CELL/PGR

(W)☎ FAX

E-MAIL

NAME

ADDRESS

(H)☎ CELL/PGR

(W)☎ FAX

E-MAIL

NAME

ADDRESS

(H)☎ CELL/PGR

(W)☎ FAX

E-MAIL

NAME

ADDRESS

(H)☎ CELL/PGR

(W)☎ FAX

E-MAIL

NAME

ADDRESS

(H)☎ CELL/PGR

(W)☎ FAX

E-MAIL

NAME

ADDRESS

(H) ☎ CELL/PGR

(W) ☎ FAX

E-MAIL

NAME

ADDRESS

(H) ☎ CELL/PGR

(W) ☎ FAX

E-MAIL

NAME

ADDRESS

(H) ☎ CELL/PGR

(W) ☎ FAX

E-MAIL

NAME

ADDRESS

(H) ☎ CELL/PGR

(W) ☎ FAX

E-MAIL

NAME

ADDRESS

(H)☎ CELL/PGR

(W)☎ FAX

E-MAIL

NAME

ADDRESS

(H)☎ CELL/PGR

(W)☎ FAX

E-MAIL

NAME

ADDRESS

(H)☎ CELL/PGR

(W)☎ FAX

E-MAIL

NAME

ADDRESS

(H)☎ CELL/PGR

(W)☎ FAX

E-MAIL

NAME

ADDRESS

(H) ☎ CELL/PGR

(W) ☎ FAX

E-MAIL

NAME

ADDRESS

(H) ☎ CELL/PGR

(W) ☎ FAX

E-MAIL

NAME

ADDRESS

(H) ☎ CELL/PGR

(W) ☎ FAX

E-MAIL

NAME

ADDRESS

(H) ☎ CELL/PGR

(W) ☎ FAX

E-MAIL

NAME

ADDRESS

(H)☎ CELL/PGR

(W)☎ FAX

E-MAIL

NAME

ADDRESS

(H)☎ CELL/PGR

(W)☎ FAX

E-MAIL

NAME

ADDRESS

(H)☎ CELL/PGR

(W)☎ FAX

E-MAIL

NAME

ADDRESS

(H)☎ CELL/PGR

(W)☎ FAX

E-MAIL

NAME

ADDRESS

(H) ☎ CELL/PGR

(W) ☎ FAX

E-MAIL

NAME

ADDRESS

(H) ☎ CELL/PGR

(W) ☎ FAX

E-MAIL

NAME

ADDRESS

(H) ☎ CELL/PGR

(W) ☎ FAX

E-MAIL

NAME

ADDRESS

(H) ☎ CELL/PGR

(W) ☎ FAX

E-MAIL

NAME

ADDRESS

(H)☎ CELL/PGR

(W)☎ FAX

E-MAIL

NAME

ADDRESS

(H)☎ CELL/PGR

(W)☎ FAX

E-MAIL

NAME

ADDRESS

(H)☎ CELL/PGR

(W)☎ FAX

E-MAIL

NAME

ADDRESS

(H)☎ CELL/PGR

(W)☎ FAX

E-MAIL